48
DETOX

Other books by Jane Scrivner

48 HOUR DETOX

TWO DAYS TO A NEW YOU

JANE SCRIVNER

PIATKUS

Copyright © 2002 by Jane Scrivner

First published in 2002 by
Judy Piatkus (Publishers) Limited
5 Windmill Street
London W1T 2JA
e-mail: info@piatkus.co.uk

The moral right of the author has been asserted

A catalogue record for this book is available from the British Library

ISBN 0 7499 2362 8

Text design by Paul Saunders
Edited by Barbara Kiser

This book has been printed on paper manufactured with respect for the environment using wood from managed sustainable resources

Printed and bound in Great Britain by Mackays of Chatham Ltd

For Mum.
Much of who I am is because of you.
Thank you.

Contents

Introduction

48 Hours in Heaven

IN JUST 48 HOURS you can cleanse, invigorate, sort, centre and pamper yourself with a programme tailor-made to your own needs. Pack yourself off on Friday night to your 'home spa' and emerge on Monday morning totally invigorated and ready to face the world.

With the help of your 48-Hour Detox toolkit, you will have all you need to put a full stop on everything that has gone before, and start the future with a fresh and positive outlook.

The 48-Hour Detox is about spending quality time with yourself, doing what you want, when you want it. About treating your body to wonderfully luxurious cleansing and invigorating treatments. About making you look and feel fabulous and planning your life so you can get back in the driving seat.

The 48-Hour Detox is not about stripping your life bare, but about adding more of the feel-good factor and a little less of the do-good factor.

And I'll show you how to do it all. In this book you'll find deliciously healthy menus, ways to relax, wonderful skin and body care treatments, little indulgences, and how to develop your creative mind or get in touch with your inner spirituality. You'll discover how to find the time to spend time with close friends, or simply shut the door on everyone else's life and concentrate on your own.

Just 48 hours to change the rest of your life, or 48 hours to realise that your life is pretty amazing already and with a bit of looking after number one, it can stay that way.

Impossible Dream?

Yes, most detox programmes are designed to work over a long period of time and yes, I fully recommend a thorough, 30-day cleanse. But I appreciate that this is not always practical or possible, or for a lot of people, even desirable. Spending 48 hours is a totally effective way to detox. Who knows, you may like it so much that you will do a larger, fuller programme.

Following a short programme of cleansing body treatments, positive mind games and nourishing spirituality tasks can indeed do wonders in those 48 hours. Look upon it as an extra powerful spring clean – a short-term exercise with long-term results.

All in the Timing

As I mentioned at the start, this detox is ideal for the weekend – Friday evening to Monday morning. But you can do it whenever it suits you, as long as you really free up those 48 hours. Choose from 7.00 pm one evening, any day of the week to 7.00 pm two evenings later. Choose any day and any time in the early evening; whenever it's good for you, it's good to do the programme.

We start in the evening so that you can do some preparation for the full following day. This also lets you start with a good night's sleep, something we hardly ever get and certainly don't include as a crucial part of our busy lives. We even aim to detox tiredness!

I've designed the programme outline so it's relatively set. This will help because it means you don't have to think of a single thing – except when you are asked to do so.

There are loads of lovely things to get you back on track, refreshed, renewed and reviewed. It is as important to include as many activities as you are asked to do: simply doing nothing for 48 hours may sound like your idea of heaven but actually structuring the time and getting things done and sorted is much more productive – and actually much more refreshing and relaxing.

There is a range of choices for every treatment session, and for each menu there are substitutions for vegetarians and a few suggestions for different appetites and tastes.

What to Expect

While there are plenty of alternatives on offer, there are also strict rules – yes, rules – for the things you absolutely, definitely must do, without doubt and without hesitation, repetition or deviation.

To get the best out of the 48-Hour Detox, browse through the book from start to finish to get the general picture. This should also kick-start your imagination on how you choose to follow your 48-hour plan. You could aim for total balance, or focus more specifically on body, mind or spirit. It's your choice.

You will then need to decide if this is something just for you, or if you want to share it with your friends or partner. You must be careful here. Your friends cannot come along for the ride; they must genuinely do the programme too, to contribute and participate. This is not *just* a nice way to spend the weekend. It is a way to put a full stop on what has gone before and to start what is going to be your future. This does not mean that you have to stop everything that you currently do and totally change. But it does mean that everything you do after your 48-Hour Detox is what *you want to do* and is working towards *what you want in your life.*

Once you have decided whether you are going it alone or with anyone else, you need to schedule the date or time. I have nothing against spontaneity; in fact, I positively encourage it. But this one needs a little planning.

If, when you browse through the programme for the first time, you genuinely believe you have everything you need to do a good job of the programme, then go right ahead and do it any time. If you know that you need to put some thought into getting all the tools for the job, then planning is key. We will look at planning vis-à-vis the programme. Perhaps the way you approach the programme is a good example of how you approach your life – rushing in where angels fear to tread, or 'slow and steady wins the race'.

Assembling Your Toolkit

Now that you've chosen a date, you need to get the tools for the job. To assemble them, get a notepad and pencil. I've mentioned that it's a good idea to read through the whole book before you begin your detox. As you do that, jot down the tools as and when they arise. Start with the general list of materials on pages 21–2 of 'Choosing Your Treatments'. After you've chosen the treatments you want, go through 'The Programme', starting on page 25, and write down all the relevant items for each one. This includes the compulsory treatments. You'll find all these items in the 'Tools for the job' boxes. You will probably already have a number of the items on your list. If not, your friends probably have them to borrow – and failing that, you may have to do some retail therapy.

'The Programme' also contains recipes for meals you'll be eating. Write down the ingredients for your choice of meals as you go through them. You can shop for them shortly before your programme begins as nothing will go off in just 48 hours. The amounts are for one, so simply times by the number of participants to have enough to get you through the weekend. Treats are included, so you really don't need anything other than what is on the list!

As you read, you'll see the treatments are split into three sections – body, mind and spirit. You can choose most of the treatments but we have put in three that you *must* do to keep the programme in balance.

How You'll Feel

First, you'll need to slow down, relax and clear away the 'stuff'. Your body needs to have time to breathe again. You need to get your foot off the accelerator and get rid of anything excess to requirements. You'll eat healthily from the very start, have a cleansing body treatment, dump all negative thoughts from your mind and prepare to focus on yourself. This is the essential first step – it has to be, we have no time to lose.

By Day Two you'll be just about ready to get back in control, and just about relaxed enough to turn your focus to the future, get back some enthusiasm, feel some energy, inspire the mind and be excited about the future. You can choose from many treatments, facelifts, exercise, breathing and thinking. You'll do some planning and some filing. You'll look at things you want to add into your life to get better quality, not just more quantity.

By lunchtime on Day Three, you are totally empowered to face the world again – but hold your horses and savour these moments of quiet and contemplation before you launch the new you. You can finish the 48 hours by spending it alone or you can get friends around. You don't have to announce anything, you can just listen to the responses you generate.

The new you may surprise some and amaze others, but most importantly, the process should leave you feeling happy and in the driving seat. You don't have to decide to embark on a huge journey. You don't even have to know exactly where you are going. You just have to want to do whatever you do next.

And it doesn't end there! You can take 48 hours off whenever you wish. You could do it every year; you could do three totally different versions (body, mind or spirit); or you could never do it again. Keep the book and dip into it every now and then. If you have a free evening do some of the treatments and invoke the feelings of the original weekend. If you have a day and a night, you can cleanse or recharge. You will know the bits you need to do, so go right ahead and use this book any way you want to.

Budget or Blow It?

The 48-Hour Detox programme is designed to take place in your home or the home of a friend. All the treatments and exercises are explained in detail so that you can make sure you have everything you need to do it all yourself for relatively little expense.

A lot of the fun of doing the 48-Hour Detox at home is to see just how easy it is to transform your own house into your very own private spa and then back again, with very little effort and disruption.

If the DIY approach does not appeal to you or budget is no obstacle, you can decide to do your own 48-Hour Detox while visiting an actual spa, or by booking into the relevant treatments at your local beauty salon, health centre or complementary therapy clinic.

If you do this, compare the spa's professional treatment list with the treatment menu in this book, and book in for the closest options available. You will probably find that the treatments for the mind and spirit aspects are less easy to come by but that should be no problem. Simply take yourself off to the relaxation room or the quiet room, and you can do these tasks just as you would at home.

The only thing that could be a problem is the smudging – burning bundles of aromatic twigs. The smoke they emit would set off most commercial fire alarms. So use pebbles or bells to clear your room instead! (You'll find out about all this on pages 30–4.)

Some people prefer their homes for detoxing and some people prefer and are able to choose a spa or hotel with treatment rooms. Whatever your choice and whatever your budget, there really is no excuse for not finding those crucial 48 hours.

The 'Treatment Brochure'

One of the most exciting parts of going away to a spa or a hotel with a health centre is the bit where you get to sit down and go through the brochure, choosing all the wonderful treatments you are going to book in for during your stay.

Booking ahead not only ensures that you get the treatments you want at the times you want them. It also means that you can tailor your visit to your own needs. If you are going away to relax, then there is little point leaving it until the only treatments or sessions with spaces are kick-boxing and outdoor aerobics. I totally appreciate that after having done either of these activities you will have no problem being able to relax, as you will have given your body the chance to work out all your tension and stress. But it's not quite the same as a soothing, cleansing body wrap with a wonderful head massage to follow.

In the same way, if you are going away to work on tension and stress and the only treatments available are a pedicure and waxing, it is not ideal. (I do agree that sometimes it can be hugely stressful to have unwanted hair and chipped toe polish, but you get my drift...)

So investing some time before your 48-Hour Detox to prepare yourself and choose your therapies will ensure that you have the equipment available and the treatments you want to have a fabulous and productive time. If you haven't already done so, get out that notebook and pencil, and go through 'Choosing Your Treatments'.

Remember, the treatments are split into body, mind and spirit. There's a compulsory treatment in each category and as you'll see in 'The Programme', these have already been inserted into your 48-Hour Detox schedule. This means you are free to determine the focus of your 'stay' yourself, to include more body treatments, more boosts in mental clarity or more spiritual exercises. But you will still finish the 48 hours in total balance.

CHAPTER ONE

Choosing Your Treatments

Now you're ready for final preparations for your 48 hours in heaven. You'll already be familiar with the treatment menu below – you chose your treatments from it so you could assemble all the items you need. Remember there's one compulsory treatment per category (mind, body and spirit), and six more of your own choosing. Now you have to decide where you want the treatments to go in your programme schedule (see pages 27–9).

Following the treatment menu in this section is a list of final preparations you need to do before you embark on your weekend. When you've done all that and it's time to begin, you'll follow the guidelines that start on page 30. This section contains step-by-step instructions for the overall detox; you'll find the detailed procedures for your six chosen treatments in the 'Treatment Manual' that starts on page 85.

The Home Spa Treatment Menu

Body

● COMPULSORY TREATMENT

Thermotherapy Shower and Fruit Drench

This treatment, using alternating temperatures, can cleanse and tone your whole body – inside and out. One of the most detoxifying treatments on the menu, this will have you jumping and cleansing for joy – sometimes quite literally. Once you have boosted your circulation, it is time to improve moisture and exfoliation. Using the fruits of your choice, you will cover your body in your very own astringent fruit acids, exfoliate with the full contents of the fruits and then wash them all away. This treatment leaves you refreshed, invigorated, exfoliated and totally nourished – not bad for a morning's work. The effects last for days.

• TREATMENTS YOU CHOOSE

Indian Head Massage
A very popular treatment, and rightly so. Indian head massage combines head, shoulders and neck work to stimulate the brain, relax the scalp and nourish the roots of the hair. All strokes are designed to drain towards the lymph nodes, resulting in a fabulously hypnotic and relaxing detox experience.

Indian head massage will reduce headaches and eyestrain, and correct postural aches. Oils can be used, or the treatment can be done dry. If you blend a wonderfully relaxing selection of essential oils for this treatment you'll take it to another level.

Foot Bath and Reflexology
By first warming your feet in a fragrant floral footbath, you can effectively treat the whole body through the meridians and energy channels accessed via the feet. This wonderfully relaxing treatment will leave you balanced, but with a spring

in your step. Working the meridians will stimulate lymph flow and internal cleansing. The oils will accelerate this cleansing, leaving you in total balance.

Balinese Lular Blush

Bring the pleasures of the Orient to your own home. This treatment will have you in the pink. You start with a total body massage using floral oils and a nourishing body oil, to relax and stimulate lymph. Then you cover your body in the lular blend – a mix of spices and oils – and wait for it to dry. You then slowly peel it away to reveal the new you. The lular spices are deeply warming and will increase your circulation and boost the action of your liver and kidneys. You will moisturise all over with natural, live yoghurt and then to finish you will relax in a warm bath full of rejuvenating and replenishing rose petals and rose oil. The Balinese lular blush is the ultimate in exotic home-cleansing treatments. You may never recover from the experience!

Nourishing Honey Buzz

With this treatment, your skin will glow and you will feel good enough to eat. This simple but highly effective facemask is all you need for a twice-weekly facial treat. Honey has long been used as a curative and is coming back into fashion. It can neutralise toxins, treat stomach ulcers, and relieve gastric illness or upset. It can bring down high blood pressure and it can help move along constipation. It can also make your skin feel wonderfully soft and nourished. Quite simply, it is a detox elixir.

A blend of honey and lemon or honey and lime, with added sesame seeds, is painted over your face and neck. The mix is rinsed off by splashing your face with both warm and cool water until the skin is left feeling moistened and nourished.

The 15-minute Facelift

Fifteen minutes of your time for a lifetime off your face! This simple face massage and set of facial exercises will stretch and tone those hundreds of facial muscles that we take totally for granted and never pay a moment's attention to – except when they let us down. 'Character lines' will become a thing of the past, and a radiant glow will glide you into the future.

Manicure and Hand Massage

We use our hands all day long, to hold, to help or to throw into the air in despair. This total hand treatment will slough, massage, moisturise and work the whole body. Not only does it feel wonderfully luxurious but just as with foot treatments, hand massage can stimulate the entire body. There are specific reflex points so that you glow both inside and out.

Mind

● COMPULSORY TREATMENT

Just Say No!

How much do you do that you would rather not? How many times do you do something or go somewhere because someone else wants you to and you don't? How many times do people take you for granted because you always say yes – are you a sure thing without being totally sure it's what you want? A few simple steps will ensure that from this moment forward, you are allowed to say 'No'.

● TREATMENTS YOU CHOOSE

Mindfulness

This workshop will take you away from the times when you wish away today in favour of tomorrow, when you worry about what may never happen and when you travel off in your imagination to a place where nothing goes right and everything is a problem.

Mindfulness is an exercise that will show you how to detox your mind. It will banish worrying about what may never happen and cease any endless dwelling on things past. The only thing we can truly rely on is the now. It is the only thing we know we have.

Staying in the moment is the secret to being mindful, but what is the secret to staying in the moment?

Feed Your Mind

Many foods can cleanse and detox and many foods can boost your alertness, improve your memory and give you that real feel-good factor.

This treatment will give you the foods. All you have to do is make the blend to improve your mind! This fabulous way to use brain cells to boost brain cells will have you concocting the most delicious brews... we hope.

Winning the Lottery

We can dream about 'what ifs', we can get out of the moment and live in a fantasy world or we can have dreams that become reality. This mind task will look at the motivations behind your wildest dreams and then show you how you can make them very real. Life can be rich, even if your bank balance is poor.

Spirit

● COMPULSORY TREATMENT

Mandala Meditation or Medicine Wheel

See how creating your own mandala can let you see your own life on every level. Explore what makes you tick and what you are made of, then celebrate. Using age-old techniques we can use medicine wheels and mandalas to clear away the waste and concentrate on the important aspects of our lives. Take a look inside and see how life doesn't get in the way but can show you the way. Getting some ritual into your life can move a lot of the waste out.

● TREATMENTS YOU CHOOSE

Altar Building

A place to go when the world doesn't understand you. A spiritual, exhilarating, playful and fabulous way to get your own personal space. You can construct a huge altar or just find a place to sit in the garden. You can use your imagination or you can just go with your instincts. Altar building is about representing your own place to just 'be'. Permanent or transient altars are a shrine to peace and tranquillity, reinvention or invigoration.

Dowsing

Develop your own dowsing skills to help you make decisions and clear your thoughts. Use this ancient practice to help you move forward by getting your answers from your surroundings. Dowsing will help you 'tune in' to exactly what you need to know and exclude any confusion or doubt. It may take some time as you learn to trust your personal oracle but soon you won't leave home without it.

Moon Meditation

The moon is incredibly powerful. It has mystery, it has strength and it has energy. Tapping into the moon can give you the same essential qualities. Use the phases of the moon to strengthen your every move and see how your own personal guide in the night sky can help you on a day-to-day basis.

The Final Preparations

Even though the programme lasts just 48 hours, you will need to do some serious preparation. If you're going to take it easy, having everything to hand makes it even easier. But that takes planning. You've already been listing items you'll need for specific treatments and recipes. The list below includes things you will need whatever you choose, as well as the items from the compulsory treatments. Read them through, as you want to avoid duplicating any items.

The General List

* Tidy rooms – bedroom, lounge, kitchen and bathroom. Then there's no temptation to tidy up.

* Warm rooms. Put the heating up a notch as you will be wearing a dressing gown and loose clothing for 48 hours. Or make sure you have the materials to light cosy log fires in the rooms you are in.

* A diary or notepad.

* Pens and pencil and/or crayons.

* Freshly washed dressing gown, housecoat or warm pyjamas.

* Freshly made bed with crisp, clean sheets/covers.

* Somewhere to sit with your feet up – a sofa with cushions, an armchair with a footstool or a day bed or chaise longue.

* A duvet or rug.

* Selection of reading material – to your taste, but nothing work-related.

* Clean fluffy towels, hand and bath size.

* A route to walk from your home.

* Lots of pillows.

* Nightlights or just a selection of normal candles.

* Relaxing music.

Items for Compulsory Treatments or Scheduled Activities

* A sage stick (see page 32), sweet grass, two medium stones or some little Tibetan bells or bowls – any one item will do.

* A fan, a feather, a piece of paper folded into a fan shape or a bunch of leaves tied together.

* Natural sea salt.

* Flower petals.

* Selection of fresh fruits – a large papaya or a large mangos or two large peaches or a medium bowl of strawberries.

* Two old towels or an old sheet.

* Paper or card, coloured pens, glue, any items from around the house, or from the garden and home. (Read the section on mandalas to give you an idea, see page 58.)

When You're Ready

Make sure you've bought in all the food on the list you made (see page 6).

Starting your detox at 8.30 pm on the Friday allows you to go home, and arrive ready to detox. Starting at 6.30 pm will mean a mad dash to get there and an overstressed start to the 48 hours.

Get home from work or being out, change into comfortable 'weekend' clothing and finish all your odd chores and tasks.

Then:

* Make sure the house is ready to begin.

Then make sure that:

* The heating is turned up a notch.

* The candles are lit in the room you are in.

* The phone is off the hook.

* Your dressing gown, housecoat and/or pyjamas are warming on the radiator.

* The water is on and hot enough for your treatments.

* The bed is fresh and ready.

* The towels are warming in the airing cupboard or on the towel rail or radiator.

* The music is playing quietly in the background.

Now you can relax into the programme starting with your space clearing and then melt into the warming bath to wash away your day...

CHAPTER TWO

The Programme

Time to Begin

DURING THE FOLLOWING 48 hours you'll be giving your body a break. It will let you see just how good you feel by investing some time and thought into looking after number one and show you that detoxing really is worthwhile. Hopefully you will feel amazing once you have cleansed away the worries and pressures of your life and worked on your body, mind and spirit. You may even decide that the results are so great that you'll undertake a longer programme – say,

30 days. If not, the 48-hour programme will at least remind you how it feels to be relaxed, to spend some time on yourself and to finally get things in proportion. To be able to just take a moment to see what takes priority and what isn't worth worrying about any more.

So, congratulations for finding 48 hours to concentrate on you. Lock the doors, put the answerphone on and switch off the mobile. This two-day plan will transform you from the tired and worn out 'human doing' on Friday afternoon to the most revitalised, refreshed and regenerated 'human being' on Monday morning.

The weekend is designed to make you feel as if you have truly gone away to an oasis of calm and comfort to be pampered back to balanced health and mentality. In order to feel like your break is just a moment away, I have taken the liberty of including the schedule for your 48-hour stay.

First Evening

8.30 pm

Space Clearing

Candle Bathing
10.00 pm: Early Night.

Day One

Awake/Lemon juice and hot water

Compulsory Treatment 1:
Thermotherapy Shower and Fruit Drench

Breakfast
The 'Relaxation Lounge'

Chosen Treatment 1

Mid-morning Snack
Yoga Stretch
The 'Relaxation Lounge'

Lunch
Country Walk to Indulge the Senses

Compulsory Treatment 2:
Mandala Meditation or Medicine Wheel

Afternoon Tea

Chosen Treatment 2

The 'Relaxation Lounge'
6.30 pm: Supper

Chosen Treatment 3

9.30 pm: Lights Out

Day Two

Awake/Lemon juice and hot water
Refreshing Power Walk
Stretch and Relax

Just Say No!

Mid-morning Snack
Relaxation Session/Lymph Drainage

> *Chosen Treatment 4*

Light Lunch

> *Chosen Treatment 5*

20-minute Power Snooze

> *Chosen Treatment 6*

Prepare for evening or friends arriving
6.30 pm: Light Supper for Friends, Partner or Family
10.30 pm: Lights Out

Next Morning

Arise, breakfast
Emerge, '48-hour' detoxed

Step-by-step Guide

First Evening

Space Clearing

There is little point starting the 48-Hour Detox if you are sur-rounded by negative thoughts, mess, dirty clothes, yesterday's dishes or the children's toys all over the floor. If anything is destined to make you realise you are at home and surrounded by the trappings of your everyday life, this will be it.

To get the most out of your detox you need to do some-thing that puts a full stop on the week/month/life that went before, and open the door to new opportunities, experiences or simply space for relaxation that you are about to create.

The best way to do this, to ensure you get the best out of it, is to clear your space in total preparation for your 48-hour programme. You'll have tidied the house the day before and done all your washing, dishwashing and ironing. Now you'll need to get ready for the ritual of space clearing – a different process, and the first step of the programme.

Tools for the job

You will need one of the following (you can have all of them but only one is necessary): a sage smudge stick or sweet grass bound together or two medium stones or some bells, Tibetan or handheld.

You will also need: a feather fan or any other kind of fan (a decorative one can be used), a feather you have found in your garden or a bunch of large leaves bound together at the base. Some natural sea salt is good – you can borrow this from your treatment supplies – or some flower petals.

Clearing is about getting rid of any negativity present. On all levels, ground (body), room space (mind) and ceiling (spirit). This might have been around for a long time – even from the previous owners of the property – or it might have been caused by some harsh thoughts or words spoken just a moment ago. Clearing will absorb them and dissolve them, leaving the area 'clear' for you to move forward.

Just as this applies to a room or a place, it can also apply to an individual. For the clearing in this context we can look at room clearing and personal clearing.

If you are not convinced that there is a spiritual aspect to this practice, there's a practical one – quite simply, your home will be tidy and just as you burn a candle to get rid of a bad smell, you will be burning herbs or making a noise to disturb or burn away the bad energy. Try it and you will feel some benefit, whichever angle you look at it from.

Fact box

Sage is a herb used for cleansing in Native American rituals. Sage essential oil is extremely cleansing and as such is actually contraindicated for pregnant women. Wild sage or white sage is best. Make your own smudge stick by picking and drying sage leaves on their twigs. If you don't like the smell you can bind together some lavender or cedar twigs, dry them out in the airing cupboard in the same way and use them as you would burn incense.

So on that first evening, when your home is ready, you can now clear the space.

You should try to clear the air on all levels, and you can bring all of the tools listed on page 31 into play. Clearing the air at floor level helps to clear the body of any negativity or stagnation. For this we use natural sea salts or flower petals scattered around the corners of the room on the floor.

Clearing the air at waist level represents clearing the mind of negativity and general thought processes. For this you will need some kind of bell or natural objects that you can bang together to make a noise – a drum would do or you can clap, or tap stones or pebbles together. Whether tapping, chiming or clapping, build up a quick rhythm. It must be quick as it needs to clear the space, not gently nudge! Then stop, and stay in that place until the resonance of the bells, stones or your claps has finished and you can no longer hear the sound. Move a few paces on and chime, clap or tap again.

To clear space higher up – which symbolises the spirit – you need to burn your chosen herb or incense: the smoke rises to the very corners of the room. Light the smudge or incense stick with a match or lighter. It will catch, but won't burst into flames due to the high oil content of the sage leaves. If there are flames, gently blow them out until the stick is gently smoking – it is the smoke you want. Pick up the feather, fan or leaves and use these to 'fan' the smoke. This will also ensure the stick stays alight.

If you are using sage or incense, walk around the perimeter of the rooms in your home, fanning the smoke up into the corners. The key areas to clear are down in dark corners – there will be stagnant energy here, and in areas as high as you can reach – and behind furniture. Walk from room to room and imagine that the salt, sounds or smoke is absorbing all negativity and wiping the slate clean.

Once you have cleansed the whole area, it is time to smudge yourself. Pass the smoke up your left-hand side and over your head and down your right-hand side, then fan the smoke away.

Once you have completed your task, place the base of the fan and the base of the smudge stick down together on the floor or tabletop and say a quiet 'Thank you'. Then you can stub out the smudge stick or incense in a bowl of sand or soil. Don't blow it out as this will simply fan it alight again.

You are now clear for your 48-Hour Detox – no baggage, no negativity. Prepare for take-off.

Candle Bathing

Now that your home is cleared and the energy balanced and refreshed, it is time to wash away the troubles of the week and to cleanse and turn your attentions to yourself. The smudging will cleanse your environment, but you also need to flush all the negativity from yourself.

Tools for the job

You will need to place a notepad and pen or pencil by your bedside, and have enough hot water in the tank to run a full bath. Then concentrate on placing candles in the bathroom. Nightlights, perfumed candles, candles in a candle holder or candles placed in bowls of sand – it doesn't matter what size they are; in fact a few differently shaped candles will look really good. This could be your chance to trawl around the house to use all the candles that sit there but are never actually used. You will also need a towel ready for when you get out of the bath to dry yourself off – treat yourself by warming the towel on a rail or radiator. Have a body moisturiser ready. If you wish to add essential oils or bubble bath or salts to the water you are welcome to do so , but the candles and the bath are the most important factors for this treatment.

Pour yourself a glass of still mineral water and drink it slowly. You are aiming to cleanse your body totally during the 48-Hour Detox. Drinking hydrates and flushes out the insides. Run a bath of warm water – not too hot as you are going to sit in it for at least 15 minutes (longer is preferable). This bath is not for you to wash yourself physically with soap and water, but to wash everything away symbolically and let it flow freely down the plughole.

Place the candles around the bath, wherever is safe. Do not place candles under curtains, or where you will be getting in and out of the bath, but in places where you can see them in front or to the side when you sit in the bath. Use enough to keep the room warm and gently lit – a minimum of three. If you do not have space around the bath, you may find you have space on surfaces like the toilet seat (lid down), or bring in a small table to place alongside your bath. Place three candles in a prominent place where you can easily see them. These three will represent the past, present and future and your mind, body and spirit.

Get into the bath and feel the water surround your body, warming and relaxing your muscles and mind. Once you have relaxed for 5 minutes or so, look at the candles you have placed in front of you. Take 1 or 2 minutes with each candle. At the first, concentrate on your past, think about how you feel about it, try to sum it up in one sentence and say it out loud. Then move on to the second and think about your life now, in the present and again, sum it up in one sentence or thought and say it out loud. Then move to the third and say what you would like for your future life, in just one sentence or thought.

Then start again with the first candle and this time sum up your thoughts on your body, mind and spirit. Say this out loud. The secret is not to dwell too long on these thoughts. Just say what comes to mind – it is often the most truthful and insightful. Spending too long on this is likely to result in over-analysis – not to mention a cold bath.

Once you have put your thoughts out in the open, they will be much easier to think about and to deal with. Now it is time to just duck yourself down into the water, covering your head if possible if you are comfortable with that, and then get out of the bath and pat yourself dry.

Once you are dry, turn to the bath and pull out the plug. Watch as the water spirals down the plughole and away. Then turn to the three candles. Blow them out one at a time and watch the smoke spiral upwards to nothing.

Now you are cleansed, and you have six thoughts to take with you for the rest of the 48-hour programme. These six thoughts will form the basis of your detox. They address every aspect of you: your body, your mind and your spirit, and your past, present and future. There is nothing else to you – just these six aspects and facets.

This will make any of the exercises or treatments that you do over the next two days more relevant as you can home in on the aspects that mean the most to you.

Moisturise your body lavishly with your favourite body cream to seal in the goodness. Blow out any remaining candles in the bathroom and then get into bed. Just before you turn the light off, write down your six thoughts so you can look at them tomorrow and not dwell on them tonight.

Early Night

You should not be in bed any later than 10.00 pm. Turn the light out and enjoy how fresh and warm the clean sheets feel…

DAY ONE

This morning you can wake whenever you wish, but please stay in bed until 9.30 am. It's not as if you need an excuse to have a lie-in, but there are several reasons for this.

Being given permission to stay in bed will take away any of the worry or even guilt that you should be up and about 'doing stuff'. Sometimes it is good to make yourself do nothing. We fill our minds with things we have to get done, people we must see, jobs we must sort, and thoughts we must think.

We hardly ever force ourselves to do nothing. We hardly ever hear the phrase, 'I'm doing nothing this weekend' or 'I'm not going to think about anything for the next few days'. This is often thought of as bad or negative. In order to relax your mind and detox yourself of negative thinking and putting pressure on yourself, now you are positively expected to lie there and just DO NOTHING. Snooze if you like, drift in and out of sleep if you must, but otherwise DO NOTHING.

Lemon Juice and Hot Water

At 9.30 am you can get up to make yourself a cup of hot water and lemon. You can go back to bed to drink it, or you can get up for good – whatever you wish. If you aren't going back to bed, you will need to take your notepad with you. You'll be using it later.

Put on your clean dressing gown or housecoat and go to the kitchen and make yourself a cup of hot water with a good squeeze of lemon juice – a quarter or half of a lemon is enough. This is an excellent way to start the day, as well as a great alternative to the stimulant of caffeine in coffee and tea.

Fact box

The organ that's vital in detoxing is the LIVER, so starting the day with a squeeze of fresh lemon juice in a cup of hot water will cleanse your palate and help to flush out the liver. The lemon is also alkaline-forming, which will help to balance your body's pH.

• COMPULSORY TREATMENT 1: THERMOTHERAPY SHOWER AND FRUIT DRENCH

This shower will boost your circulation and invigorate you. You'll use fruit, which acts as an exfoliant – even though it is not rough, the fruit acids slough away the dead skin cells. The alternating water temperature will have you buzzing for the entire day.

Tools for the job

You will need a warm bathroom, a shower, a mixture of fresh fruits from the list below, mashed together in a plastic bowl, two old towels to stand on and cover yourself in, and one clean dry towel.

> **The fruits**
> Small punnet strawberries, one large papaya, one large mango or two large peaches. Remove any leaves and large stones but do not peel.

Place one old towel outside the door of the shower. Place the bowl of mashed fruits somewhere easy to reach while standing on the old towel.

Get into the shower, and turn on the water to nice and warm. Let the water flow over your body until you are relaxed and warmed through. Then turn the shower to cold. Stand under the cold water for a count of ten, making sure the water runs down your back and front from the shoulders down.

Switch the water to hot again and let your shivers disappear. Once you are warm again, turn the shower to cold. This time make sure your head is under the water as well and count to fifteen. Then turn to hot again. Repeat this at least three more times, making sure that you are fully warm until you flip back to cold, count to fifteen and flip back to warm. Once you have done this five times, finish with a cold splash and turn the water off. Step out of the shower on to the old

Fact box

Fruit pulp contains enzymes that soften and revitalise the skin. They also exfoliate dead skin cells and smell divine. It's Nature's way of getting AHAs (alphahydroxy acids).

towel. Scoop up some of the fruit pulp and slowly paste it all over your body. You should feel your body warm up, as your circulation has been given a real kick-start.

Once you have covered your body, leaving space around your eyes and mouth, you need to wrap yourself in the second old towel and wait for 10 minutes – this is why you need a warm bathroom. The fruits will be cleansing and exfoliating and nourishing to your invigorated skin.

When the time is up, get into the shower and make sure you rinse off all the fruit pulp. There is no need for soap, just water. Get out of the shower and dry yourself with the clean, warm towel. Get dressed in loose, casual clothing.

Why do you feel so fantastic? The alternating-temperature shower is cleansing, invigorating and refreshing – think of all your tension and stress just running off your body and down the plughole. The combination of hot and cold increases circulation, tones muscles and reduces muscle tension. It will even make you look younger! All this in just a few minutes. The fruity drench is included to moisturise, exfoliate and nourish your body. (They always say that fruit for breakfast is good for you.)

Breakfast

Now it's time to dip into the fruit bowl again. You'll be breakfasting on mixed fruits, natural live yoghurt, oatmeal and unsalted, natural nuts and seeds. Pick the ones you want and prepare them for your breakfast. Fruits are high in nutrients, containing large amounts of essential vitamins, amino acids and minerals. They are high in fibre and potassium. They contain very little waste and very few calories. Fruits are nearly all goodness. Raw fruit is raw energy, and cleans the gut efficiently.

Natural yoghurt is good for the intestines and the oatmeal will make you feel satisfied. You need the nuts and/or seeds to increase the protein content and balance your breakfast. You can have a medium-sized bowl full of any, some or all of the above. It is your choice, but you must sit down to eat it and make sure you chew it thoroughly.

The Relaxation Lounge

By now it should be around 10.30 am and after all that activity it is time to relax. Watching TV or reading the newspaper or your company newsletter is not the way to relax; you need to experience some escapism. Detox your day of all things related to work, business or anything stress-related, and spend your time generating normality, peace and tranquillity. You will need a good novel, or a magazine full of fun articles or frivolous nonsense. You will need to go to your 'relaxation room' and get comfortable with your feet supported just higher than your hips to help circulation, your back supported with cushions or pillows, and a nice warm blanket or duvet tucked in around you. You will need to spend at least an hour relaxing. If you drift off to sleep, that is fine, but make sure you relax and aren't tempted to do anything – it is amazing how we have forgotten what being relaxed actually feels like.

Chosen Treatment 1

You are now ready for your first chosen treatment. The detailed description of how to carry out your treatment is in the 'Treatment Manual' on page 85. Have fun and enjoy the experience.

Mid-morning Snack

Once you have completed your first chosen treatment, you should have a mid-morning snack. Several small meals are better than two or three big ones so now is the time to have a couple of pieces of fruit and a handful of nuts and or seeds. You should also take this chance to have a cup of hot water – warming, refreshing, cleansing and hydrating for your body and skin. Remember, this is just a snack. You are about to do some stretching, so a full stomach would not be comfortable.

Yoga Stretch

Yoga and stretching are forms of exercise that will tone your internal and external organs and muscles. Depending on the versions or types of stretch or yoga you choose, the exercise can be gentle, slow and relaxing, or focused and actually quite strenuous.

If you are familiar with stretch exercises or already attend or have attended a yoga class, then this is the time for you to put into practice what you already know. Spend 20 minutes stretching or carrying out your yoga routine. If not, or if you want to follow instructions so that you do not need to involve your mind in deep thinking at this stage of your detox, then please do the following exercise and repeat it three times.

Sun Worship

You should follow the instructions carefully, and if at any stage you find the moves difficult or outside your 'stretch' range, just slow down and keep within your comfort zone. Remember, this is not an excuse not to push your body, just a sensible precaution so that you don't damage yourself.

* Stand with feet shoulder distance apart. Bend your knees slightly and just bounce yourself lightly, rocking from the balls of your feet to the heels and swinging your arms gently by your side. This will feel as though you are preparing to jump forward from a standing position – exactly right, but with no jump.

* Breathe deeply through your nose and down into a relaxed belly. Exhale slowly and steadily. Continue to breathe in a relaxed way.

* Bring the palms of your hands together in front of you and lift them slowly until they are directly over your head. If you can, push the stretch slowly until your hands are leaning back past your head. Do not strain anything, just stretch everything.

* Now bring your hands forward slowly and roll down to meet your feet, feeling each vertebra stretch as you roll

down until your hands touch the floor on either side of your feet. Alternatively, just take the stretch to as low as you can manage.

* Let your body flop and your neck relax with your head hanging down.

* Once in the 'bent double' position, move your left foot back until it is in the biggest stretch behind you with your right foot and both hands in a line on the floor in front of you. This will feel like a lunge and the stretch should be in the front of your thigh.

* Now raise your head so that you stretch through your back and neck.

* Lower your head to level with your shoulders and pull your left foot forward and then your right foot back so that they meet a little past your hips. This stretch will feel like a cat stretch: your back is arched and your head down. Feel the tension in all the muscles as you hold the stretch.

* Lower your body down to touch the floor. You should be lying level with the floor but still supported by your hands and knees.

* Push with your hands to straighten your arms and stretch your stomach muscles. Roll your neck and head back as far as you can, and hold the stretch.

* Do the whole stretch again, but in reverse to get back to a relaxed standing position...

* Lower your body flat to the floor.

* Walk your legs up together to the cat stretch, arched back, hands in front of you and feet behind you.

* Lunge your right foot backwards and leave your right foot between both hands in a line in front of you.

* Pull your right leg up into line with your left leg and stretch into the bent double position.

* Roll your spine up slowly to lift your arms to over your head and past your shoulders.

* Bring your arms back to above your head and then lower them to the front of your chest, palms together.

* Take a deep breath and repeat twice more.

This stretch will move through each and every part of your body from head to toe. It will expand your lungs and increase your deep breathing and will calm and relax you as you salute the sun.

The Relaxation Lounge

Retire to your relaxation lounge with your notepad. Have a look at the six sentences you wrote in it last night, describing your past, present and future and your body, mind and spirit. Sit for 5 minutes with your eyes closed and check in with your body and how you are feeling. Make sure the room is quiet and when you have experienced how you feel, write down six more sentences against the categories exactly as you did before. Don't think too much. Just write down what comes into your head. Reread yesterday's thoughts and see if anything is changing: are you getting things into perspective? Close the notepad and do some reading for 15 minutes before lunch – you deserve it.

Lunch

Detox food can be wonderfully exotic or very basic. Fresh, raw or lightly cooked ingredients leaving every nutrient in will feed your body energy and goodness. Keeping the foods we eat pure and fresh will mean that we use every last part of our food for energy and growth. Eating additives, preservatives and toxic chemicals means we use our energy for processing what we eat and getting rid of most of it – probably with no nutritional gain at all.

You should choose *one* recipe from each column. This will ensure that whatever your tastes, likes and dislikes, you still have a good choice. By sticking to the food as shown you will definitely get a deliciously and nutritionally balanced meal.

Column 1	Column 2	Column 3
Grilled fillet of fish of your choice	Nutty brown rice	Mixed green salad
Fluffy goat's cheese	Herb rice	Broccoli and almonds
Kidney bean and red onion salad	Beetroot and green bean coleslaw	Courgettes and watercress

Fillet of Fish

   1 piece of fish

Take a piece of fish (any cut is fine and oily fish is best), and grill until cooked through and the skin is nice and crispy. This usually takes just a few minutes each side.

Fluffy Goat's Cheese

   4 oz soft goat's cheese
   1 tablespoon natural yoghurt
   coriander or fresh parsley

Take the soft goat's cheese and the natural yoghurt: goat's is best but normal cow's yoghurt is fine. Mix the two together by adding a teaspoon of the yoghurt, folding it into the cheese and then adding another teaspoon until all the yoghurt is blended in. Then, using a small balloon whisk, whip the cheese until it is light and airy. Finely chop some coriander and fresh parsley or any thin-leaved herb of your choice and fold into the fluffy cheese.

Kidney Bean and Red Onion Salad

1 red onion
1 small can kidney beans
1 dessertspoon oil of choice
½ lime
freshly ground black pepper

Chop the red onion into fine slices. Rinse the can of kidney beans and mix with the onion. Add a dessertspoon of any oil of choice and then squeeze the lime over everything. Season with some freshly ground black pepper.

Nutty Brown Rice

1 handful dry brown or red rice
1 tablespoon natural almonds or hazelnuts

You can actually use brown or red rice for this course. Cook the rice as instructed on the packet. This normally takes about 20 to 30 minutes, as both red and brown rice are quite hard and need to be softened down a lot. While the rice is cooking, get the tablespoon of natural nuts, almonds or hazelnuts and crush them together. The easiest way to do this is to put them in a small plastic bag and gently bash with a rolling pin or solid object. They do not have to be ground down too much but should be at least broken into quarters. Then, taking a small non-stick frying pan, lightly toast them over a low heat. You do not need any oil for this and you will know they are done when the smell of roasting nuts is given off. Drain the rice when it is cooked and mix together with the nuts.

Herb Rice

1 handful dry brown or red rice
1 bunch herbs, such as coriander, chives or basil

Follow the instructions above, but instead of toasting the nuts you need to chop the herbs finely. You can choose any you like but coriander, chives or basil are favourite recommendations. Once the herbs have been chopped and the rice has been cooked, combine them and mix well.

Beetroot and Green Bean Coleslaw

2 or 3 cooked beetroots
1 handful green beans
1 tablespoon natural yoghurt
1 teaspoon poppy or nigella seeds

Take the cooked beetroot and slice into pieces half a centimetre thick. Steam the green beans and slice each bean in half. Mix together with the beetroot and put the natural yoghurt in the mix. For extra flavour you can add a teaspoon of poppy seeds or, if you can get hold of them, some nigella seeds.

Mixed Green Salad

green salad leaves
olive oil
½ lemon
½ lime

Prepare the salad by placing any green salad leaves – rocket, lettuce of any sort, lamb's lettuce, chopped celery, watercress – into a bowl and drizzle with olive oil. Take the lemon and lime and squeeze the juice of both over the leaves.

Broccoli and Almonds

5–6 florets broccoli
1 handful flaked almonds
1 teaspoon oil

Steam the broccoli florets until tender. Toast the flaked almonds in a shallow, non-stick pan. Add the oil and the cooked broccoli, mix with the almonds and fry until quite brown.

Watercress and Courgettes

2 courgettes
1 handful watercress

Slice the courgettes into thin ribbons and either stir-fry or place on a preheated griddle. Turn halfway through, and cook till they are golden brown or striped. Mix with a handful of watercress.

To serve, place your three choices on a plate. Now, eat your lunch nice and slowly. Savour every mouthful and see if you can detect all the wonderful flavours, the herbs, the fish, the cheese, the salad, the oil and citrus juice. . . and remember, it takes 20 minutes for your stomach to tell your brain that it is full, so eating slowly ensures you don't overeat. Don't do anything else while you are eating. Don't watch television or read a book. Simply take the time to have a meal.

Country Walk to Indulge the Senses

After lunch you can go for a walk. If it's cold, wrap up warm; and if it's hot, make sure you have protection from the sun. Ensure you actually experience what you see. Just be with nature. Hug a tree – see what it is that people joke about, and see how it feels. Stop and actually look at a flower, its petals, its centre, its stem, its perfume – yes, actually smell the fragrance; don't just think that you know it smells nice. Take the time actually to bend down or reach up and smell the perfume for yourself. Think how wonderful it is that nature just makes a thing smell so nice so that it can survive. Just take this time to go out and about and see, feel, touch and smell for yourself.

The next treatment is the making of your own medicine wheel or mandala, so keep your eyes peeled for anything you may want to collect along the way. If you chose to build your own altar later in the programme, when you leafed through 'Choosing Your Treatments', you may want to keep that in mind too. I don't mean for you to go out picking flowers, but to gather old twigs or petals or seashells, depending on what is around you while you are enjoying your walk. Even if you are walking in the inner city you may be surprised at how much nature is around you – feathers, leaves, twigs, pebbles and much more.

It is traditional to go for a walk after lunch to allow the food to go down. So there is nothing for it but to go outside to get some fresh air. It's still one of the best ways to blow away the cobwebs. Taking a walk gives you time to actually see what is going on all around you. We spend so much time 'doing' our day-to-day lives that we rarely take time to 'be' in our lives. Whatever is going on, good or bad, easy or difficult, the flowers still grow, the wind still blows, the sun comes up, the moon comes out, the rain falls and feeds the earth, the clouds scud across the sky, the night falls, the stars come out and then day breaks.

There is nothing we can do, nothing we can say, nothing we *need* to do and nothing we *have* to say to make any of it happen. Nature is constant; it happens every day and all around us. Focus your thoughts on your surroundings. Don't take them for granted – start to notice even the smallest flowers or the slightest change in temperature. Even in the bleakest of weather or the wildest of storms, nature just happens and goes on happening. Nature is amazing but we never stop to see, to drink in the changes and the constants. Earth, water, air, fire and metal are all completely natural and from the earth. Everything we do in life comes from these natural elements but we don't pay any attention to it.

• COMPULSORY TREATMENT 2:
MANDALA MEDITATION OR MEDICINE WHEEL

Looking at mandalas will help you to focus on your own life and to see how you can get back into it – how you can become involved in your own life and where it is going instead of being the innocent bystander.

Have you ever felt that you are not part of your own life, that you are not in control or in the driving seat? Everything seems to happen around us or go on about us and we are simply being washed along without really taking an active part.

Tools for the job

How do you make a mandala? You can do it with crayons on paper, you can do it with paint and a canvas, you can do it with sand on a beach, you can do it with beans on the kitchen unit, you can do it with stones or leaves in your garden...

The only thing you do need to do is to create a wheel, circle or flow that represents everything important to you in your life. The representation doesn't have to be a picture, it could be a colour or shape or it could just be a place that you go to that is your place, your own personal mandala.

The word mandala means circle and centre. Mandalas can represent the whole world or your whole life. They can depict your most explicit desires or your innermost and deepest thoughts. They also serve to remind us that nothing, absolutely nothing, happens in isolation. Everything we do and everything we are is connected to an ever-increasing and never-ending circle. By following the 48-Hour Detox you will change nearly everything in your own life and the lives of those around you.

Think about it – if you were not doing the 48-Hour Detox, this might be your weekend:

* You go to the supermarket on Saturday morning to get some food to eat to help you recover from the night before at the pub or club.

* You could then spend an hour ironing clothes.

* Then some time tidying up in the house.

* Then you call a friend to arrange to go out with the children to the zoo tomorrow.

* Then you sit and watch a television programme you pre-recorded.

* Your friends arrive and together you make supper.

* You take a call from a work colleague who is working this weekend.

* You wash and change.

* You share supper with your friends, while the kids watch a video.

And so on...

But as you are doing the 48-Hour Detox, the above would not have happened and you will have changed everyone's lives.

* The barman would not have served you, but they could have served someone who they have now become good friends with.

* The owner of the bar would not have made profit from you so may not be able to buy or do something they were planning to.

- The supermarket would not have sold you bacon and eggs so the shelf stacker wouldn't need to replace what you bought, which may have given them time to have a conversation they might not have had.

And so on...

We can see mandalas in many natural things, or we can create our own. It is the representation of the continuous flow that we concentrate on. Many cultures use mandalas or circles to represent the total circle of life, birth and then ceaselessly spinning to death which gives rise to birth, and so on.

The 'circle of life', 'this mortal coil'. These are phrases that show how we think of life as either a visual or actual circle or sphere.

The Chinese believe that Yin and Yang are two halves of the whole, representing male and female, dark and light, sun and moon, hot and cold, fast and slow. Everything in the energetic cycle of Chinese beliefs is depicted with the dovetailing Yin and Yang symbols. One feeds off the other and vice versa.

Buddhists believe that we can exist in any lifetime in any form, and this is reflected in their mandalas. They create visual mandalas or pictures that show the many paths to enlightenment. The drawings or paintings are true depictions of the journey to enlightenment and understanding. There are circles within circles and each is used for meditation and thought.

Native Americans use mandalas to represent the wheel of life. The Native American mandala is also called a medicine wheel. This wheel is marked out in the compass points north, south, east and west; the four seasons spring, summer, autumn and winter; and the four elements water, earth, air and fire.

It seems that whatever your belief, you can use the imagery of the circle and the power of nature to create your own personal mandala or medicine wheel. We are able to focus on our own life, our own beliefs and our own path to achieve and create whatever we wish to.

You should now set about designing your very own mandala or medicine wheel.

There are no rules! You do exactly what you want to do to create your own mandala, your own circle of life. But here are some suggestions.

You can get paints and paper from the local stationery shop and draw a circle. Within that circle draw the things that represent your life: children, partner, work, friends, partying, reading – anything you like. Then place the finished mandala somewhere where you can focus on it or spend time looking at it. You may wish to keep it private or you may wish to pin it on the fridge door so that you can take a deep breath, look at everything that is important to you, take another breath and then get on with your day.

If you don't feel confident drawing anything, take a leaf out of the Native Americans' book and draw your mandala in sand or from nature.

Go out into the garden or park and collect twigs, leaves, gravel, soil, seeds. Make a pattern with these items from nature or simply make a circle within which you can sit and spend time thinking. Set it at the bottom of your garden and look back at your home or set it on the doorstep and look out at the world, whichever best represents you in the centre of your own life.

Or you could follow this principle at home. Go to your cupboards and get maybe four or five different powders, granules or seeds – a tablespoon of coffee, a tablespoon of tea (open a tea bag!), a tablespoon of breakfast cereal, a tablespoon of sugar and a tablespoon of lentils or flour. These are all different colours and you can now begin to make a pattern with them on the kitchen unit or on a piece of paper covered in a thin film of clear glue, if you wish to keep it. You could make a spiral of the granules in increasing size, each type of food depicting different aspects of your life, cereal for family time, flour for growth, coffee for excitement, tea for relaxation – anything you want.

Once you have your mandala, look at it, sit in it or gaze towards it. Then you should take 15 minutes to contemplate yourself. Take a deep breath down into the very bottom of your lungs and let the air flow out of your mouth. Be with your mandala and look or meditate on each area that needs work, or even just needs you to consider it for the first time in ages. You can ask yourself some questions while you are with your mandala. These might be:

* Is the mandala in balance? Will my wheel spin evenly or is it spinning out of balance?

* Have I forgotten something or put too much of something less important in the cycle of my life?

* Have I drawn or represented a true picture or have I distorted it?

* Is it all in dull colours or bright colours?

* Do I smile when concentrating on some areas and do I find it difficult to look at other areas? Do I actually avoid some of the areas completely?

Afternoon Tea

Once your mandala or wheel is completed, it is time to turn your thoughts to tea. You have the choice of any herbal or fruit tea you like and you can have as much as you like, sip slowly and savour the flavour. Create your own tea ceremony.

Chosen Treatment 2

You can now follow the instructions for your chosen treatment 2, from the 'Treatment Manual'. Be sure to have everything to hand.

The Relaxation Lounge

You now have time to totally relax. After looking at each aspect of yourself, you can put it all to one side and just nourish the frivolous side to your life. Choose a favourite TV programme or film, curl up with a book or simply snooze. Make sure you keep warm and concentrate on just how nice it is to be doing something you want to do, not for anyone else except yourself – be absolutely selfish and self-centred for the next hour and a half. Don't feel guilty about doing nothing. Positively expect to do nothing and enjoy every minute of it. Each time a thought enters your head that is not to do with how you are feeling or what you are doing right now, then just let it pass right through. Concentrate on yourself, how relaxed you feel, how good the book is, how enjoyable the film is, how cosy you feel, how wonderful it is to just relax and re-energise – feel good right now.

Supper

You should now be ready to glide into the kitchen and prepare a delicious supper. Make sure you lay the table and have a comfortable seat. You should also endeavour to eat by 6.30 pm – and no later than 7.00 pm. This will give your body time to digest your food before you go to bed. This should help you get a better, deeper night's sleep.

You have two options for supper. Both are delicious and both require some preparation. This is deliberate, to show you how easy it is to cook at home and how nice it can be. The 48-Hour Detox is about getting rid of toxins, waste and negativity, but that is not to say that you shouldn't add things to your life to truly detox. The opportunity to create a meal for yourself or friends is very relaxing if planned well or kept very simple. Pottering about in the kitchen to your favourite piece of music, loud or quiet, can be a lot of fun – and might just result in a delicious and nourishing meal.

Your choices are Thai prawn soup with a spicy vegetable grill, or roast vegetables and seared chicken breast.

Thai Prawn Soup

>   selection of vegetables
>   stick of lemongrass
>   1 chilli pepper
>   vegetable stock cube or fish stock
>   1 teaspoon of oil
>   4oz fresh prawns
>   goat's or sheep's yoghurt
>   fresh coriander

Chop all the vegetables, place in a pan and just cover with water. Bring to the boil with the lemongrass and halved chilli and the stock cube. Mix thoroughly together and simmer until the vegetables are tender. In another small pan, add a teaspoon of oil and gently fry the prawns. Cook for a few extra minutes until the prawns have gone a good pink colour and are slightly browned. Remove the vegetable pan from the heat and pour the stock into a bowl. Remove the chilli and lemongrass, then blend the vegetables together. Add the stock and yoghurt to make a soup-like consistency. When your spicy vegetable grill is ready (see below), heat the soup again, stir the prawns into the soup and add the chopped coriander before serving.

Spicy Vegetable Grill

large portion mixed vegetables
1 small beetroot
1 teaspoon freshly crushed ginger root
crumbled goat's cheese

Preheat the oven to 180°C/350°F/Gas 4. Slice the vegetables into thin strips. Place them in a large preheated, ovenproof dish. Stir in the crushed ginger and sprinkle the goat's cheese on top. Bake in the oven for 40 minutes until the vegetables are tender and the goat's cheese nicely browned.

Roast Vegetables and Seared Chicken Breast

1 large courgette
1 large leek
1 red pepper
1 red onion
1 tablespoon olive oil
sprinkle of sea salt and freshly ground peppercorns
1 teaspoon cumin seeds
1 skinless chicken breast
1 lemon

Heat the oven to 220°C/425°F/Gas 7. Chop the vegetables into 1-centimetre chunks or slices. Place a baking tray in the oven and once it is hot, add a tablespoon of oil to the tray. When the oil is hot remove the tray from the oven and put all the vegetables on the tray, mixing around to make sure the oil has coated the vegetables. Sprinkle on the sea salt, fresh pepper and cumin seeds. Place in the hot oven and check after 20 minutes. While the vegetables are roasting, cook the chicken breast by either grilling for 10 minutes on each side or cooking on a griddle. Alternatively, you can put the chicken breast on the baking tray with the vegetables, but you must turn it after 10 minutes.

After 20 minutes check the vegetables. If they are browned and crisp, remove. If not, leave for a further 10 minutes, but remove the chicken as soon as it is cooked – you do not want it to dry out. Once the vegetables are done, remove them from the oven, squeeze the lemon juice over them and put them all on to a warmed plate. Place the chicken breast on top and serve.

For dessert you can have a choice of goat's cheeses with celery and grapes. Do not have biscuits. Just taste the thin slivers of cheese and the different textures with the juice of the fruits and the crispness of the celery.

This will be your last meal for 18 hours. You are now embarking on a surprise mini fast to help speed up the 48-Hour Detox. The programme is not very long, so we need to find a way to pack in as much cleansing as possible without making you rush or feel under pressure to get everything done.

By leaving 18 hours between meals, you should feel your body clean and empty through without giving the metabolism the chance to slow down due to lack of food supplies – we are sneaking it in so that it goes relatively unnoticed. Just when the hunger pangs strike you will be able to tuck in to a deliciously refreshing and welcome meal.

Chosen Treatment 3

Now is the time to have your final evening treatment. It is entirely up to you if you wish to have a body treatment to wash away, slough up and polish down, to expand your mind from the mind section or to see if you can find a new experience in the spiritual world. You will obviously have just eaten, so think about that when you decide on which treatment to choose.

If you have managed to schedule supper for no later than 7.00pm and taken time with your final treatment, it will probably be around 9.30pm by now. You can now decide how to end your day from the following two options:

Option 1 Read a book for no more than an hour.

Option 2 Write a short story that you could use to tell a child at bedtime. It doesn't matter if you don't have children or don't know any children, that is not the point. See how wild your imagination can run in just 30 minutes. You can then decide if you do want to read it to anyone or simply put it aside as your own personal bedtime story.

Lights Out

Once you have read or written a story, it is time to turn in for the night. Snuggle down, lights out and sweet dreams.

DAY TWO

Lemon Juice and Hot Water

You packed a lot in yesterday so today's timing is up to you. You may want to sleep in or you could wake quite early with bags of energy depending on how you were feeling before you started your 48-Hour Detox. You should listen to your body today and do just as it asks.

If a lie-in is required, go right ahead. If you want to get up and out then make sure you have your drink first.

Start with your fresh lemon juice and hot water as you did yesterday. No food this morning except a bunch of red grapes to munch on – a medium-sized bunch is good. You have already slept through half of your mini fast – the best way to fast in my book.

Dress slowly and warmly if required in preparation for your early morning walk.

Refreshing Power Walk

Take a refreshing walk. You are likely to be feeling hungry, but remember the walk yesterday and take the time to look around you and have a look at what is growing and what is changing. The only difference is that you can make it a power walk and bring the pace up to a brisk walk. While walking, see if you can notice a difference in just 24 hours – what has come out and what leaves have fallen, what birds are around and what city-dwelling animals have padded around in the early hours.

Stretch and Relax

Follow the stretches from yesterday to waken and salute the sun. Feel your body and lungs expand, take in refreshing air and exhale stale, used air. Check in with your body. Do you ache a little from yesterday, or does it feel a little bit easier perhaps? You will be surprised at how much you actually remember and how different you feel.

Just Say No!

'No' is one of the smallest words in our vocabulary but can have a massive impact. We worry about saying no to someone much more than we do about saying yes.

Imagine how easy your life would be if you just said no when you didn't want to do something. Imagine how clear of clutter and detoxed you would feel if you were able to get rid of all the jobs you have taken on and time you have wasted by not being able to say no when you really wanted to.

One of the main reasons we won't say no when we really want to is not because of ourselves, either – it is mainly because we don't want anyone to think badly of us.

This next exercise will help you to find a way to say no if you want to, and to see that saying no is not as bad as it seems.

- Get yourself comfortable and take out your notepad and pen.

- Think for a few moments and then write down the last five times or occasions when someone said no to you.

- Have a think for 5 minutes, and then list the first five things that spring into your mind that you didn't want to do but did, or that you have arranged to do and would really prefer not to. Basically, what have you said yes to recently, when you actually wanted to say a big resounding NO?

- And now write down the last five occasions when you said no to someone – not the children when they were doing something dangerous, but a genuine 'No, I don't want to' or 'No, I cannot'.

* Now look at the lists and alongside the first list make a note of what you did when you were told no.

* Write down alongside the second list why you wanted to say no or why you want to say no.

* Write down alongside the third list what they said when you said no.

* You may start to see some patterns emerging. When someone has answered no to you it has not made you hate them, refuse to speak to them or expel them from your list of friends. It may have been a problem for a few seconds but as soon as the answer is given you will be thinking of alternative solutions or alternative options. The no is probably forgotten as quickly as it was said. You move on and the world keeps turning. In fact, you probably totally agree that it would be difficult for them and you fully understand why they said no. No harm done.

* Now look at the list when you have said yes where you should have said no. Work out how much time was or will be spent of your life doing something you don't or didn't

want to do. Now you can see just how much time you spend that could be your own time for doing what you want to do. You may not be able to go back on your word for the things that you have said yes to but read on in the exercise to learn how to say no more effectively in the future.

• The times you have said no to someone, just as when they said no to you, the world has not stopped or it is unlikely the person has never spoken to you again. It is more likely that they have accepted the response or have found an alternative solution. They may have tried to persuade you, but if you still said no then you will see that you are living proof that you can survive.

NO is not such a big deal

If you still have doubts, here are some ways to say no and stick with it. Three are firm when you say no and mean no. Two are a little softer for the times you mean no but want to be able to say yes as long as it suits your terms. Remember: they all mean no.

Just say NO
By saying no, people will immediately see that they must

reassess their situation. This is not your problem, you have simply taken away one of their many options. You were asked and your answer is no. Don't apologise or give a reason. If you mean no then that is all you need to say. Don't give them any chance to find a fact that they can use to persuade you to say yes against your better judgement. Just say no.

Understanding NO

Say no, indicate you understand the situation so that they see that you know and understand the importance of what is being asked of you but that you are still saying no. There is little confusion in this firm version of no. No, I know you need a babysitter, but I am unavailable at that time or no, I understand you need that document typed by tonight but I am unable to reschedule my workload for you.

NO with a reason

If you explain why you are saying no, just use a short explanation; if you keep adding reasons they turn into excuses and then it seems possible to persuade you – watch out for this one, because a cunning player will start to find alternatives to your reason so that you are now available to say yes!

Repeated NO

If you say no and they won't take no for your answer then keep on saying it until they finally do. Don't raise your voice or walk away – just say no to each request, quite calmly and they will eventually get the message.

Then there are the times you have to say no but are happy to find a way to say yes.

NO, not now, but...

If you are asked to do something that is no for now but could be yes at another time. No, I am sorry but I can do... or No, I cannot help with that but I can do this... or No I cannot but how about...

These clearly state that the original request is unacceptable but you are open to negotiation. Remember that this is a compromise, not you eventually changing your plans to fall in with the original request.

You should look at your own behaviour, how good are you at actually accepting no for an answer or are you as guilty as your friends or colleagues of not respecting the meaning of this word. Do you try to reorganise their life to get what you want...

Now rehearse the new ways you have to say no… The more experience you have the easier and more effective you will find it.

Mid-morning Snack

You are still on your fast, but you will be feeling a bit peckish so another bunch of grapes and some water or herbal tea is fine if you wish. If you are not hungry, just have some water while you go on to the relaxation session.

Relaxation Session with Lymph Drainage

You won't need to be talked into this session; you will probably feel relaxed and nicely tired. We have just taxed your brain so take it easy. Remember that you have not had anything to eat today, so please make sure you have had some water or herbal tea.

Fact box

The lymph system is the body's waste disposal mechanism. It takes stuff from your blood and body that cannot be processed easily and breaks it down into smaller, more manageable sizes and then passes it back into the system for expulsion. Your blood system has the heart that acts as a pump to make the blood flow, but the lymph only moves around your body when your muscles contract and your body moves or is elevated. The better the lymph flow, the more efficiently the body is cleansed.

Go to your relaxation lounge and make sure your feet are propped up with pillows or cushions until they are higher than your hips. This will ensure that the lymph is helped to flow while you are sitting still. It is normally pumped around the body as you move your muscles, but putting your feet up will mean that gravity is doing the job just as well.

Chosen Treatment 4

We are zipping down the list now – you should be becoming a total spa professional. Enjoy your session.

Light Lunch

Lunch should fall after 1.00 pm, which will make the time since your last meal 18 hours later. Don't be tempted to wolf down a whole load of food. Just make a light meal from the following ingredients. Keep it simple because you are going to be pushing the boat out this evening, either with friends or family or just with your own company.

* Grilled fish of choice or grilled skinless chicken breast

* Salad of tomatoes, radishes, cucumber, beetroot, onions of any sort, celery, lettuce, watercress, fresh coriander, nuts of choice, beans of choice but not baked.

* Dressings – olive oil or nut oil, lemon or lime juice, plain live yoghurt.

The fish, chicken or nuts are your protein and the carbohydrate content of this meal is restricted to vegetables. This is because rice, which is the normal detox carbohydrate due to its scouring and cleansing qualities, will feel too heavy on your stomach after the mini fast. Plus we are just extending the benefits of the fast a little until supper.

Chosen Treatment 5

Use this treatment to start your preparation of body, mind or spirit for the evening entertainment.

20-minute Power Snooze

You must take this snooze, and you must restrict it to 20 minutes. Set an alarm if you need to. If you sleep any longer, you will feel groggy and find it difficult to get up and if you don't do it you won't find out how good it makes you feel later this evening. This is a snooze; don't thrash around thinking you cannot sleep. Get into a comfortable position on the bed, armchair, wherever you wish, keep warm, just close your eyes and relax for 20 minutes. You may drift off, you may not, but relaxation and replenishment are key here.

Chosen Treatment 6

Again, ensure you get the full benefits as preparation for tonight.

Light Supper for Friends, Partner or Family

Now all you need to do is prepare a lovely meal to eat by yourself, or to share with friends, partner or family. Make sure you eat before 7.30 pm to allow you to digest your food before going to bed. Don't stay up too late: you should be in bed by 10.30 pm. But you should listen to your own body, and if you feel tired before this then bid your friends a good evening, thank them for coming and take yourself off to bed.

Here are a few suggestions for the menu. I haven't included recipes, as these are simple grills and fruit concoctions. Remember that whatever you choose should be light, as you are now fabulously honed, detoxed and ready for anything the world has to throw at you. You have tucked into food for thought, you have nourished your spirit and you have fed your body for the last 48 hours.

Menu 1

Olives to nibble

Grilled sardines and dried apricots on a rocket salad

Apple and summer fruit slices with chilled goat's yoghurt

Menu 2

Assorted nuts to nibble

Grilled salmon and cod with courgettes and mange tout

Fresh fruit and goat's and sheep's cheese selection

Menu 3

Crudités with goat's yoghurt, onion and mint dip

Savoury brown rice with tuna flakes

Strawberries or fruits in season

Lights Out

Remember – get to bed no later than 10.30 pm.

Next Morning

Having finished your programme and had a nourishing night's sleep, you should start the day with a wonderful nut crunch muesli or fresh fruits muesli – whichever you prefer.

While you sip a cup of hot water and lemon, mix together seeds, nuts and fruit – fresh or dried with natural goat's or sheep's yoghurt. Tuck in. Chew slowly and taste the raw energy. What a great way to start the day.

Well done. You have successfully completed your 48-Hour Detox. Now you have cleared the decks and straightened your thoughts, just watch what can happen to the newly refreshed, cleansed and detoxed you.

CHAPTER THREE

Treatment Manual

I N THIS MANUAL you'll find step-by-step instructions for all of the 'free choice' treatments in the 48-Hour Detox. Instructions for compulsory treatments are in 'The Programme', as they arise over the course of the 48 hours.

Body

Indian Head Massage

To get the best from an Indian head massage, use a massage oil blend for the treatment and then a rinsing solution when you have finished the process. This will mean a little extra washing after the treatment, but will nourish the hair and scalp and give you beautifully shiny hair as well.

Tools for the job

Mix 10 ml of oil; sweet almond, jojoba or plain sunflower oil will work well. Add to this oil three drops each of lavender, tea tree and geranium essential oils. Mix together.

Wear an old T-shirt, as the oil is likely to drip on to your shoulders or your hands, and protect any surfaces where you will be sitting. If the room is warm enough you can do this with no top on, and then any oil from your head will moisturise your skin as well.

* Slowly pour the oil into your hair and comb it up over the scalp with a wide-tooth comb. Make the strokes up and over the top of your head to ensure your hair is totally covered in oil. When it is mixed in, you can start the massage.

* Sit down in a chair with a back support or sit comfortably with your back straight. With your right hand gently squeeze the muscles of your left arm. Start at the nape of

the neck and squeeze handfuls of flesh down your neck, over the shoulder and down to your wrist. Squeeze firmly and slowly. Repeat for the other side.

* Lean your head slowly to the left, stretching your neck muscles. Hold for the count of five and then repeat for the other side. Then lean forward and feel the stretch start a little down your back, where the neck muscles begin.

* Sitting upright, place both hands on the scalp on either side of your head (as if you are blocking your ears), lift the hands off your scalp leaving only the tips of your fingers in touch with your head and push firmly into the flesh. Massage firmly pushing the skin across the surface of the skull and not working through your actual hair. You need to stimulate the deeper muscles, so push firmly and slowly in small circles. Once you have worked an area you can move the ends of your fingers slightly and start the process again until you have covered all the area of your head. Move rhythmically and slowly and keep your shoulders relaxed.

* Now release the skin from your fingertips and grab large clumps of hair in your fists and move these in slow, relaxing circles. Pull and tug the hair gently to help increase the blood flow to the roots of the hair.

* Lift your fingers on to your scalp and then tap the ends of all your fingers in a brisk movement over your scalp. You should feel the tapping movement across the entire surface of your head.

* Move your right thumb down and hook it under the ridge of your skull on the right-hand side. Push the neck muscles along the line of the skull, gently squeezing and releasing in a rhythmic movement. Repeat for the left-hand side.

* Hold your two forefingers on your temples and slowly push in with firm pressure. Hold and release, and repeat three times.

* Bring the two fingers down around your eye sockets and up over your brow bone. Slowly push the flesh all around your eyes.

* Finally run your fingers through your hair several times and when you reach the end of your hair, long or short, grab a handful and gently tug. Repeat for a few moments and relax.

* When you have finished, you need to shampoo your hair. Depending on which oil you have used and the absorbency of your hair you may need to do this twice. Once you have

completed the shampoo, rinse your hair in a jug of hand-warm water mixed with cider vinegar for dark hair or chamomile tea for blonde hair. Make sure you rinse absolutely everything off. Towel dry your hair and let it dry naturally. There's no need to use heat styling products as you are just 'at home' this evening.

Foot Bath and Reflexology

To prepare for your foot bath and reflexology treatment you will need the following tools.

Tools for the job

You will need a bowl for warm water, big enough to put both feet into, a towel to dry your feet, a tablespoon of milk, lavender, rose and ylang ylang essential oils, and lavender flowers, rose petals and orange zest.

You might also want to have massage oil or calendula powder and pumice or emery board for the feet.

- You need to fill the bowl with warm water and take it to a place where you can sit for 10 minutes with your feet immersed in it. Put the tablespoon of milk in a small bowl and add two drops of lavender, two drops of ylang ylang and one of rose essential oil. Pour this blend into the foot bath. Sprinkle the petals on the surface and drop in the zest of the orange. Placing your feet in the warm water will increase the blood flow to the feet and boost circulation throughout the body. The lavender will relax, the ylang ylang is very feminine and uplifting and the rose will rejuvenate and soften.

* When you have soaked your feet for 10 minutes you can take them out of the water and dry them off. You might want to use a foot pumice at this stage to slough away any dead skin on the heels and sides so that you can get to the pressure points more easily. Get rid of dead skin – and detox your feet!

* Now, get into a comfortable position where you can reach one foot at a time without being too contorted. Follow the sequence as described below to rub away the tension and banish the blockages:

  ○ Apply massage oil or powder to your hands if you wish.

  ○ Make contact with your foot with both hands.

○ Take a deep breath and using quite firm pressure, rub your hands all over your foot and up over your ankle to just below the knee.

○ Repeat this stroke three or four times, increasing the pressure as your hands move towards you and decreasing as your hands push away from you.

○ Working on each of your feet in turn, place the ends of your fingers together on the sole of the foot with the heels of hands together on the top of the foot.

○ Push the heels of your hands out and down over the top or bridge of the foot and repeat several times with firm pressure until you have covered the top surface area of the foot.

○ Leave the heels of the hands together this time, and move the ends of the fingers out towards the side of the foot on the underside or sole.

○ Rub both feet vigorously.

○ Place your hands flat on the sides of your feet and wiggle each foot so that all the joints between the toes and foot bones are moved against each other – as you would do to warm up cold feet.

○ On each of your feet, using your thumbs, work over the entire surface of the foot in tiny slow, deep circles. If you are using oil or powder, this stroke works over the skin as the oil or powder allows 'slipping'. If you are not using anything, the stroke pushes down on the skin and moves the skin around in small circles.

○ Now do the same stroke working on the underside of the foot. Remember, use lots of very small circles so as not to miss any of the pressure points or reflex points.

○ If you reach an area that is sore, hold on the point with your thumb or finger until the discomfort stops or reduces. Repeat.

○ Squeeze the heel between thumb and fingers.

○ Wiggle each toe along its full length, side and tip. Finish each toe by pulling from the tip with little tugs to open the joints.

○ Do some long final strokes all over the foot and up to the knee.

○ Once you have finished with one foot, wrap it in a towel and then repeat the sequence on your other foot.

○ Well done. Every last bit of you has just had a wonderfully relaxing treatment.

Balinese Lular Blush

This is a traditional Balinese treatment for brides-to-be – but you don't have to be one to enjoy this cleansing and purifying treatment. Here is a list of ingredients for your own traditional lular scrub – a DIY version to get the experience in your own home.

Tools for the job

You'll need a small soup bowl full of olive oil, 2 tablespoons of milk, 2 large tablespoons of ground rice, 1 teaspoon of turmeric powder, and ylang ylang, rose or jasmine essential oil or a mix of all three. Add a large old towel or large old sheet, a pot of natural yoghurt and a medium paintbrush.

- Mix 2 tablespoons of the olive oil with three drops of rose oil, or any floral essential oil that you wish. Put to one side.

- Mix the 2 tablespoons of milk with one drop each of your floral essential oils. Put to one side.

* For the lular blend, mix into the remaining olive oil the ground rice, turmeric and remaining oils. This should make a thick paste that you can paint over your body. If it is too thin, you can add more ground rice, but don't be tempted to add more turmeric – you may stay yellow! The rose oil is rejuvenating and very feminine and the turmeric will warm and increase your circulation for internal cleansing.

* Place the old towel or sheet on the floor. Massage the olive/rose oil blend over your entire body. Use firm strokes up towards the heart and make sure you reach all areas.

* Take the medium paintbrush and paint a good layer of the lular blend over your body. Do not wash off the massage oil; you are painting over it to help seal it in.

* Wait for the blend to dry. This may take 10 to 15 minutes depending on the warmth of the room/thickness of the layer.

* When it is dry, gently rub the surface so that it peels away in flakes or crumbles away. This is part of the treatment so should be done carefully; it exfoliates and increases circulation. You could do this on to the towel or sheet, or you could get into the shower. In that case, just rinse the remaining blend off your body.

- When all the lular blend is crumbled or rinsed away, paint the natural yoghurt over your entire body. This will moisturise and protect your skin. Wait a further 5 minutes, then shower off in warm water.

- Finally, run a warm bath, add the blend of floral essential oils and relax for as long as you wish. You're purged and cleansed, ready for the rest of your life.

Nourishing Honey Buzz

We all know how good garlic is for us. Well, honey seems to have some very similar cure-all properties. As this treatment involves coating your body in a paste, it's obvious why I've opted to use honey rather than garlic! This treatment is simple and quick but very sticky – don't rush it too much.

Tools for the job

You'll need a pot of honey. Try to get a really exotic honey from, say, eucalyptus or wild flowers. If this is difficult, a plain runny honey is fine. You'll also need the juice of two limes and one lemon, a small bag of sesame seeds and an old towel or sheet.

* Lay out the towel or sheet on the floor. Mix all the other ingredients together into a paste. Stand on the towel or sheet, simply scoop the honey mix out with your hands and smear all over your body and face. The more you rub the product in, the more exfoliating it becomes – but it will work well even if you simply wipe it over your body.

* Wait in a warm bathroom for 10 to 15 minutes. You can wrap yourself in the sheet or towel and read a book or just sit and relax.

* Then step into the shower and wash the blend off. Your skin will be nourished, soft and invigorated.

The 15-minute Facelift

You can do the whole of this treatment during your 48-Hour Detox, but you should try to do a 5-minute version at least every other day to keep your face supple, toned and wonderfully moisturised.

Tools for the job

You'll need to make rose facial oil. Take 10 ml of sweet almond, jojoba or avocado oil and add two or three drops of rose essential oil. Alternatively, use any facial product you already have – the more natural, the better. You'll also need an exfoliation product or some lemon juice, a medium paintbrush, a small pot of natural yoghurt, two hand towels and access to a tap. A small spray or mister bottle filled with rosewater is optional.

* Mix the facial oil or open the facial product of choice.

* Tie your hair back or put on a headband.

* Hold a small hand towel under the hot tap until it's totally soaked. Wring the towel out tightly and then drape over your face. You can lie down, or simply lean your head backwards slowly. Hold the towel in place until the heat has gone and your face feels relaxed. Remove it while wiping your face over once.

* Put some drops of your chosen facial product on the ends of your fingers and start the treatment.

* Wipe the oil over your face and neck and then over the front of your chest area.

* Place your hands flat over your face and exert the pressure through the fingertips. Bring your hands across your

forehead and down each side of your face, around to your chin and up to your bottom lip. Move around your lips, up either side of your nose and between your eyes, along each brow bone and back under your eyes towards your nose.

* Push your fingers back up the bridge of your nose and up your forehead. You are now back where you started. Repeat the whole process three times.

* Place both hands flat on the front of your chest and brush briskly upwards towards the chin. Repeat for 1 minute, working over the entire chest and neck area.

* Place your hands on either side of your nose, as if you were about to blow it, and push your face through your hands and let your hands push against the ears. Bring back down to the chin and repeat three times.

* Using your fingertips, brush briskly towards the nose from the edges of your face. Work your entire face for 1 minute.

* Using the pads of the first two fingers, work them in slow circles over the face, pushing the flesh gently but firmly against the bones of your face.

* Then, taking either the exfoliation product or the lemon

juice, place the product or juice on your lips and rub in small circles along both lips.

* Wash your hands and then gently tap your fingertips all over your face – as if you are drumming your fingers on a table.

* Finally, place your thumb and forefingers along the edge of your chin and squeeze the flesh along the edge up to and around the top edge of the ears. Repeat four times.

* Put the towel under the hot tap again and wring out firmly. Drape over your face and leave for a few moments. Using the palms of your hands, press the towelling into your skin and then wipe off the oil with the cooled-down towel.

* Then, using the paintbrush, paint the natural yoghurt in a fine film all over your face and neck area. Leave this to dry.

* Run the towel under the hot tap again, wring out and wipe away the yoghurt. Repeat three times.

* Run the towel under the cold tap and wring out and drape over the face a further two times.

* Pat your face and neck dry with the dry, clean towel.

* Take a look at your glowing face and spritz with the rose-water as and when you wish.

Manicure and Hand Massage

You may wish to do this as one of your 'end-of-day' treatments, as you double the benefits if you can leave your hands in the 'moisture mitts' overnight. Even if you do not do this and simply choose it as a treatment followed by a relaxation, you will still feel and see the benefits.

So, take yourself off to bed or to your relaxation lounge, and enjoy this wonderful home manicure and hand massage. It is a simple but effective way to scrub away all the dry and dead skin from your hands, to moisturise deeply and to massage and increase the circulation in them. It's a way of cherishing tools that we use all day, every day, but never give a second thought to.

Tools for the job

You will need some natural sea salt and lavender essential oil, some olive oil and a pair of cotton gloves. If you cannot get hold of cotton gloves then you can use hand towels or towelling/flannel mitts.

- Mix a tablespoon of natural sea salt with half a tablespoon of olive oil and three or four drops of essential oil.

* Scoop the scrub mix on to each hand and rub you hands together slowly at first, building to a firm 'wringing' motion. Make sure you cover the entire hand and wrist area and rub together for a couple of minutes. Leave for 1 minute and then rinse your hands gently in warm water. It is likely that there will be a slightly oily residue, but this is fine. Dip your hands into a little more olive oil and then begin to massage your hands.

* Wring your hands as if really washing them thoroughly.

* Lean your thumbs into the wrist area and in small firm circles move over the entire area of the wrist and top of the hand.

* Knead the backs of your hands with the heel of the opposite hand.

* Press the ball of your thumb on one hand down into the groove between the knuckle and wrist on the opposite hand. Drain down from each of your fingers to your wrist. Repeat for both hands.

* Lean your thumbs into the back of the hand and move the flesh across the bones in a circular motion.

- Turn the hand over slowly and lean your thumbs into the palm of the hand and move over the entire palm in small firm circles in an upwards and outwards motion.

- Pay special attention to the ball of the hand.

- Squeeze, wring and stretch each finger individually.

- Push back your cuticles in a slow, firm movement using the sides of your thumbs. Do not use another nail, as this may rip the cuticle.

- Rub your hands together one last time, then put on the cotton gloves or wrap your hands in the towels or mitts. Leave overnight or for an hour minimum.

Mind

Mindfulness

Staying in the moment is the secret to being mindful – but what is the secret to staying in the moment?

If you don't stop worrying about the future or thinking about the past, you will totally miss the present. You will never be able to enjoy or experience anything that is actually happening. You will live a life of anticipation of the future or memory of the past. The only real thing in our lives is 'now'; what has gone is over and what is to come may never happen. No matter how much that is true, we still spend most of our lives ignoring now.

Doing the following exercise will help you to realise what you are missing and show you how to start to get back into the now. If you do ever find your mind wandering while you are trying to be mindful, then as soon as you realise, just shout NOW! and that should bring you right back to reality.

Answer the following questions:

* Do you dwell on what has been said to you or about you?

* Do you worry about being on time for future appointments?

* Do you eat your supper while watching television?

* Do you read the papers while listening to the radio, or with the TV on?

* Do you feel short of time?

* Do you give an answer or start your reply while the other person is still finishing off?

* Do you worry about future birthday/family or general gatherings?

* Do you start one job before finishing another?

If you have answered yes to more than four of the above then you need to pull back and get into the moment – your moment. Otherwise you may just miss it.

How to Be Mindful

Imagine that you have been given the use of a 30-minute time machine. This means you can travel forward or backward in time for 30 minutes each day.

You don't have to use it all up, but you cannot save it up. If you take longer than 30 minutes you may just get stuck out in the ether, never to return.

You may now go on your daily journey. You must write down everything that you think of on your journey that hasn't happened yet or has happened and that you keep thinking about. You can write anything that is not to do with today, with you at this moment or with the 48-Hour Detox.

Now you need to read through the list of things you have written down. Then put a note or sign by the items indicating whether you think they are 'good' or 'bad'.

Look at all the things that you put 'good' against. It is likely that there are less of these than the 'bad' ones. Spend 10 minutes thinking about these things. Have a laugh, a giggle, look forward to them and plan for them, think about what you are going to wear, or anything you need to do to get ready for them or enhance them. Simply be aware that they are going to happen.

Now look at the items in the list with 'bad' written against them. Do exactly the same thing: they are equally important and are taking you away from the present just as much as the good things. Plan for anything you can do to make them better, or cancel them if they are worrying you badly. (See the 'Just Say No' session on page 73 if you need to!)

You may not accomplish everything in your 30 minutes, but do not worry, as you can go on another 30-minute trip tomorrow, and the next day, and so on. They can happen every day. They are your own time to go off on a journey to sort everything out.

Now it is time to come home – to just BE. You can BE busy or you can BE relaxed, but you must fully BE whatever you are doing at the time.

And that could be all sorts of things. You could eat yoghurt and blueberries or bananas. You could look at a view or walk through a flower-filled garden. You could read a chapter of your novel, watch a 30-minute TV programme, take a bath, or call a friend.

Whatever you choose to do, you must experience it totally. You may find yourself wandering off in your mind, but as soon as you do just let the thought drop or write it down so that you can visit it on tomorrow's trip. Then forget it and come back to now.

For the next two days, you should think about everything you do as you are doing it, and as soon as you realise you are doing one thing and thinking about another, just let the thought go and come back.

By the end of the week, you will have started to get back into the habit of living your life instead of wishing or worrying it away.

Be mindful of the facts...

Feed Your Mind

Using foods from the list below, you now have to get creative in the kitchen and get juicing.

All the foods listed can boost the brain and stimulate or clarify your mental processes – or just prove a real feel-good factor. The fun is not in the resulting cocktail but in the experimentation along the way! You should design one sweet and one savoury cocktail.

If juicing doesn't appeal, you can turn the savoury cocktail into a tasty soup by chopping and simmering the ingredients in vegetable stock, and the sweet version into a smoothie by adding some natural yoghurt to the blend. The properties will be similar but less potent as soon as you add heat.

The foods	What they have in them	What this does
Fresh egg yolk, celery, carrot, spinach, beetroot, onions	Choline	Aids memory
Grapefruit, cabbage	Inositol	Nourishes brain cells
Avocado, peaches	Niacin	Boosts nervous system and brain function
Bananas, stoned, soaked dates, prunes	Tryptophan	Helps the brain produce serotonin
Sesame seeds, pumpkin	Phenylalanine	Improves memory and mental alertness
Onions	Iodine	Improves speed of brain readiness and response
Basil, parsley, honey	General stimulant	Wake-up call, adds flavours

Winning the Lottery

This exercise is designed to test your imagination to the full. If you don't get to use it much, dust it down and crank it up. If you use it too much, change direction and see if you can make your dreams a reality.

> ### Tools for the job
> You'll need your imagination, a comfortable place to sit, the telephone and the local phone book or the number for directory enquiries.

Imagine you have just won the lottery

Write down the first ten things you would do with the money. We are not talking just four numbers, we are talking millions – the full six plus a bonus ball, and it was a rollover and it was also doubled to celebrate a national holiday. There is no restriction on the money, so there is no restriction on your imagination.

Now you have to imagine that you have booked in to do all these things and are really excited and looking forward to them immensely. Then a small disaster strikes and . . . you wake up.

But you did make the list, and you are still looking forward to doing the things on it. You now have to find a way to recreate your dreams with your normal budget allowance. If you are broke, you have to find a way to do something similar with no expenditure. If you have some money available, you can spend more. The only thing you cannot do is to decide that it is impossible because you don't have the lottery money. Work out the motivation behind your dream, and fulfil it anyway.

Obviously you will need a great deal of imagination, but it is still possible. Here are some ideas to get you going.

Lottery list	True motivation	...with a little imagination and even less money
Become a paying passenger on the Space Shuttle	Do something daring and exciting that you have never done before	Take a light aircraft, microlight or glider flight
Take the whole family on a holiday	Spend time giving your family a good time	Get the whole family round for the weekend, with the kids sleeping on the floor and the adults on sofas and in spare rooms. Have a carpet picnic and barbeque – even if it's raining

Lottery list	True motivation	...with a little imagination and even less money
Give some of your winnings to charity	Help others who are less fortunate than yourself	Call your local charity and see if you can help for a day or donate games, clothes or time
Wear only designer labels	Change the way you look or spruce up how you feel	Don't buy the next six items of clothes you want, and then you may have saved enough for one designer classic. Buy designer accessories and spruce up your wardrobe. Root through the jumble sales or charity shops in the nearest wealthy area!
Give up your job	Take some time off for yourself	Take a long weekend...

The final step to making your lottery dreams come true is to spend the next hour booking into your diary either the time or the appointment to fulfil your dreams. If you don't make the arrangements, you can see that your imagination is driven purely by money, and that isn't much of an imagination now, is it?

Spirit

Altar building

This treatment is all about making a place to go when the world doesn't understand you. A spiritual, exhilarating, playful and fabulous way to get your own personal space.

We tend to think of altars as something you only find in churches or religious houses of worship. This couldn't be further from the truth. In fact, I once knew someone who built incredibly stunning altars out of biscuit tins. They doubled as room dividers... both practical and beautiful.

Building your own altar is as complicated or simple as you want it to be. It can be built inside or outside. Your altar is your own place of calm and contemplation, so it needs to be built of anything that brings you calm and provides the right atmosphere for thought and contemplation.

The instructions are simple, but the actual construction may take some time. Once it is built you should keep it for some time. You can adapt it, but you should maintain it and visit it frequently. It is your own personal sacred space.

Your altar should be made from items that please you: photos of loved ones, items that interest you, objects that represent parts of you and your life. They can be items that you find and items that you have been given. They can be completely natural – in which case you may wish to go on a walk and harvest twigs, stones and feathers. Or you may want to go through your personal effects and see what you have been hoarding that is important to you.

Your altar can be a circle within which you can sit, or it can be on the floor so you can sit in front of it. It can be tall, short, square, in a line, absolutely any shape or configuration that pleases you. I think you get my drift.

When you have the materials for your altar, you need to choose where it can be. It could be in a corner of your bedroom, in your dining room, a quiet corner of your garden or at the base of a tree. Just think about a place that would be comfortable and convenient to visit each day.

Before you start building, you may want to space-clear the area (see page 30) or you may want to just sit quietly.

Be mindful as you do it. You are building your own altar, so place objects exactly as you want them. It is all part of the ritual.

When your altar is complete, spend at least 30 minutes sitting at it or in it. Study it and see how it makes you feel. Focus on each different bit and see if there is anything that needs rearranging.

You can now use your altar as a place where you can celebrate your life, meditate, be quiet, say thank you for something that goes right, or share your emotions if you need to offload. You can keep it and nourish it with items you are given or find along the way – things that inspire you to think 'That would be just right for my altar'. This is your own personal, private space and it should be kept exactly how you want it.

Dowsing

Dowsing skills help you make decisions and clear your thoughts. Using this ancient practice will help you move forward by getting your answers from your surroundings. Dowsing will help you 'tune in' to exactly what you need to know.

It will take some time at first and you certainly won't get it completely in just 48 hours. But you do have time to make a good start.

Tools for the job

You'll need a chain or thread about 30 centimetres long, an object such as a key or ring or crystal in a clasp and a piece of paper with a circle drawn on it. Draw a line through the circle from top to bottom and another from side to side. Then mark the circle with two further lines as if marking out all the compass points: north, south, east and west and the interim points, SE, SW, NE and NW.

- When you have drawn your circle, you need to construct a very basic pendulum. Tie the cord or chain to the object you are using to dowse with – key, crystal, etc.

- Now you need to 'tune in' with your pendulum. Hold the pendulum in your steady hand and ask it which is the way for 'Yes'. Then let the pendulum start to move. When you have established which way is yes, stop the pendulum and ask it which is the way for 'No'. You can then try and see if this is repeated, and you should get a confirmation of your directions.

- If you cannot tune in, you can programme your own pendulum. Simply start to move the pendulum in one direction and tell it that this is the way for yes and then stop it and move it the other way and let it know this is the way for no.

* It may not happen immediately but you do need time to tune things in to each other. It takes a while to get to know a friend.

* Once you are happy with the accuracy of your reading, you can move on to asking questions. You need to phrase questions carefully. Open-ended ones are quite hard for a pendulum to answer. There isn't an obvious swing for 'blue' if you ask it 'What colour should I paint my bedroom?' The correct question would be, 'Should I paint my room blue?'

* You will be surprised at how often you start to use your new-found dowsing techniques – and not just at parties after a few drinks to see how many children your friends will have and who someone is going to marry...

You can check to see whether food is OK to eat, you can use it to find missing objects, you can use it to see whether people will arrive on time, and much more. I have even used it to see if I was going to live in a house I was trying to buy. The answer was 'Yes', and I am now sitting in that very house writing this book.

Moon Meditation

We can use the moon to give us the strength to get things done, say things we need to say and start new projects. Not only is the moon spiritual and feminine, it also has immense energy. It dictates the movement and flow of the earth's water. We are something like 70 per cent water – and our brains are 75 per cent water – so we must be affected in a similar way. There are even words to describe how the moon can affect us: 'lunatic' comes from the word lunar or moon. If the pull of the moon is strong enough to create tides, it should be strong enough to help us detox our lives.

Tools for the job

You'll need a notepad and pen, a place to sit comfortably with your whole future ahead of you and a diary including the phases of the moon or a copy of *Raphael's Astronomical Ephemeris* (available in most good bookshops).

During every month there are four lunar phases: new, full, waxing and waning. The cycle repeats continually. Occasionally there are two full moons within one month, which is called a blue moon. That is where we get the phrase 'Once in a blue moon' for something that happens very rarely.

You can use this cycle, the power of the moon, to affect your own cycles, physical and emotional. If you are making changes in your life or wishing to bring something to a close, you can synchronise these events with a phase of the moon. So you can harness the moon's power to strengthen your actions and bolster your confidence.

The first thing you need to do is write down a minimum of six things that are important to you or that you would like to achieve, start or do. They can be anything that you would consider doing as part of your normal life. You could try for something like marrying the heir to the throne, but unless you are a member of the royal family already, that doesn't really count as 'your normal life'. We are more likely to be looking at things like asking for promotion, changing jobs, asking someone out, going away for a weekend, throwing a big party, finding a reliable cleaner or booking singing lessons. If pop idols can do it, you may just be the next hidden talent.

Once these have been written down, look at your diary or ephemeris and see when the phases of the moon fall in the next four- or five-week period. Make a note of the key dates.

Read the following chart.

New moon	Good for planning and preparation. The new moon is about preparation for new beginnings. This is the time you should formulate plans ready to put them into action in the next phase.
Full moon	Creativity, being fruitful and being productive. You are firing on all cylinders. Getting things done and being effective. This is the time to create.
Waning moon	Closure, finishing projects, ending things. Bringing things to a conclusion. Leaving things behind and moving on. Working through old ghosts and ridding yourself of them.
Dark moon	A time for meditation, contemplation and mystery. This is a time for introspection and concentrating on your self. This is the dark before the dawn.

When you have looked through the chart, look back at your list and study it to try to work out when is the best time to carry out some of the projects. For example:

* **Ask for promotion** You should plan this for a full moon. You are firing on all cylinders and have the creativity to

convince your employers that you are the one destined for the position versus the others.

* **Change jobs** The waning moon will help you leave one job and move to another, but you may want to make the final decision to go at a full moon when you will be best at making the right plans. If you leave at a waning moon, be sure to take a few days' holiday to prepare as this will fall in a dark moon. You will then have time to feel secure in making your move and that it was the right decision.

* **Ask someone out** Almost certainly a job for a full moon: think about it carefully, and then go for it!

* **Go away for a weekend** Depending on whether you want to plan, party, relax or energise, you'll need to look at the phases of the moon very carefully. Check the chart above and think it through.

When you have worked out the best times for each achievement, simply put them in the diary. This is a firm booking. Your month ahead should be exciting, and you should try to stay aware of your lunar support.

The treatment manual contains many choices. If you find it difficult to decide which ones you want to include in your

48-Hour Detox, don't worry – you can always do the others next time.

Doing a 48-Hour Detox every six months will keep you cleansed and invigorated – why not book your next break right now?

Plan to stay healthy.